This book was devised and produced by
Multimedia Publications (UK) Ltd

Editor Richard Rosenfeld
Design Mick Hodson
Picture Research Jackum Brown
Production Arnon Orbach

This edition published 1985 by Omega Books Ltd,
1 West Street, Ware, Hertfordshire,
under licence from the proprietor.

ISBN 1 85007 011 3

Extracts pp25, 62, 63 from H. David Baldridge's book *Shark Attack:*
© David Baldridge; published in USA by Berkley Publications
Originated by Clifton Studio, London
Printed by Cayfosa, Barcelona, Spain
Dep. Leg. B-36.613 - 1984

SHARKS
Killers of the Deep

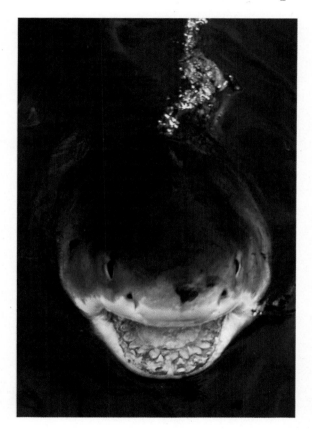

OMEGA BOOKS

SHARKS
Killers of the Deep

Michael Bright

CONTENTS

INTRODUCTION

On Sunday, 24th July 1983, the 40ft (12 m) long fishing trawler *New Venture* foundered off Queensland's Great Barrier Reef. A boom broke, the boat heeled over, was hit by a freak wave and turned turtle, throwing the 28-year-old skipper Ray Boundy and his crew, 21-year-old cook Linda Horton and 24-year-old Dennis (Smurf) Murphy, into the water.

"Smurf was on deck and jumped straight into the water", recalled Boundy, "but Lindy and I were caught in the wheel-house. We all ended up sitting on top of the upturned hull wondering what on earth we were going to do."

The trawler began to sink, and the three laughed and joked about their chances of survival as they grasped one life ring, three large pieces of foam and a surfboard to keep themselves afloat. They were confident that eventually they would be spotted and rescued. On Monday evening a shark appeared — a 15ft (4½ m) long tiger shark. It circled, nudged the life ring and pieces of foam, but didn't attack.

"We weren't worried because I'd seen sharks before. We weren't taking much notice of him, thinking that if we didn't antagonize him he might, with a bit of luck, leave us alone."

Laughter to fear

It didn't. The shark disappeared below the surfboard and came up to take a bite at Boundy's knee.

"I panicked a bit and jammed my other foot down on him and he just let go. I said to Smurf: 'We're not ready to be his dinner just yet.'"

Five minutes later another large wave knocked the trio off their rafts and into the sea. The shark grabbed Smurf's leg. "Next thing, my mate was screaming his head off. He said: 'He's got my leg, the shark's got my leg'. Then Smurf said: 'I've lost my leg', and the shark pulled him under a couple of times.

"I could see the blood coming to the surface through the water. I didn't know what to do. 'Kick him as hard as you can', I yelled."

The shark came back and began to close in.

"Smurf did the bravest thing I have ever seen. He tried to swim away from us towards the shark to divert it, calling back to us, 'You and Lindy bolt, because he'll come back for the rest of me.' When I turned round I saw the shark finish him off. As it picked up the top of his body and dived, Smurf was just screaming. I couldn't believe that anyone could have that much guts to try and get his mates out of trouble."

Second bite

The girl became hysterical, but Boundy was able to calm her down. For a couple of hours they made good headway, paddling towards the edge of Loaders Reef, and estimated that they would make landfall by morning. But the shark returned.

"Lindy was sitting in the sling of the life-ring with her feet up on the foam and I was holding her hand when I saw him come along again. He slewed around and

How the Australian papers reported the shark attack on Ray Boundy, captain of the New Venture, *and his crew in 1983.*

Daily Mirror

NEW BIG CASH BINGO GAME 6

MORE FOOD

Wednesday July 27, 1983   30c

GIRL EATEN BY SHARK!

Mum's dream of sea horror

By WYNNE GRAY

THIS is 21-year-old Linda Horton, the woman eaten by a five-metre shark off the north Queensland coast.

Linda was the maneater's second victim. The huge shark had already attacked deckhand Dennis Murphy twice before killing and devouring him after their fishing boat capsized and sank.

Trawler skipper Ray Boundy, who watched helplessly as his crew was picked off, swam for 36 hours with the shark stalking him before he reached the safety of a reef.

Today, Linda's father Noel told how his wife had dreamt

● Continued Page 3

More stories, photos P2, 3

VICTIM: Linda Horton, 21, who was taken by a shark off the north Queensland coast

WIN FREE FOOD

Previous page: *One of the most exciting challenges for a sports fisherman* (top) *is to catch a giant great white shark* (bottom). *Sometimes, though, the roles are reversed and the hunter becomes the hunted. Nevertheless, for even greater thrills some fishermen defy death and have taken to shark fishing with a fly-fishing rod and tackle from a small and vulnerable boat, often shorter than the shark itself. Large sharks, hooked and played alongside, are killed with one blast of a shotgun to the head.*

grabbed Lindy around the arms and chest.

I was still holding her hand as he shook her about three or four times, just like a rag doll, causing the life-ring to fall off. She only let out one little squeal, as soon as it hit, and I knew that she was dead. She didn't know what had happened."

Using pieces of foam Boundy paddled as fast as he could towards the reef. Just after day-break the shark reappeared.

"It was just going round and round me. I had lost my two best friends and now the shark had come for me."

8

Every time the shark came close Boundy stopped paddling and drifted until it had gone. At last he could see the reef, and a spotter plane flew overhead.

"I knew I'd be all right if I could just make the reef. I waited until the shark disappeared and used the foam to surf over the reef edge.

I was 100 yards off the reef, and the shark had followed me. It was still zigzagging about behind me."

Boundy caught a wave and was taken over the reef. He scrambled ashore, laughing hysterically. Then it all hit him and he broke down and cried.

Clinging to life

Ray Boundy's tragedy was undoubtly one of the most horrific shipwreck and shark attack stories in Australian history, and was almost a re-run of an incident in Moreton Bay, 10 miles (16 kilometres) to the north of Brisbane in March 1977 when three fishermen were thrown into the water after a freighter had sliced their boat in two. For 36 hours the men clung to a floating ice-box, but just 45 minutes before their rescue the sharks arrived. Small ones bit at their bodies, and the blood and commotion attracted a 19½ft (6 m) long great white shark, known locally as the white pointer. Two of the fishermen were killed and one survived by climbing into the ice-box.

Both stories quickly became front page news in national newspapers, were widely covered on radio and television, and were reported in considerable detail in newspapers all over the world. They had sparked off that primeval fear we have of creatures from the deep, in particular the terror of a shark attack.

Psychiatrists suggest that much of the concern with dangerous animals stems from Man's shadowy and distant past when our ancestors came down out of the trees and faced a most terrifying threat — that of being eaten alive.

Of all the mankillers, it seems, we are most terrified and fascinated by the shark. Few divers who have looked up and suddenly faced those unblinking, black, expressionless eyes and a mouth bristling with rows of serrated teeth would argue with that.

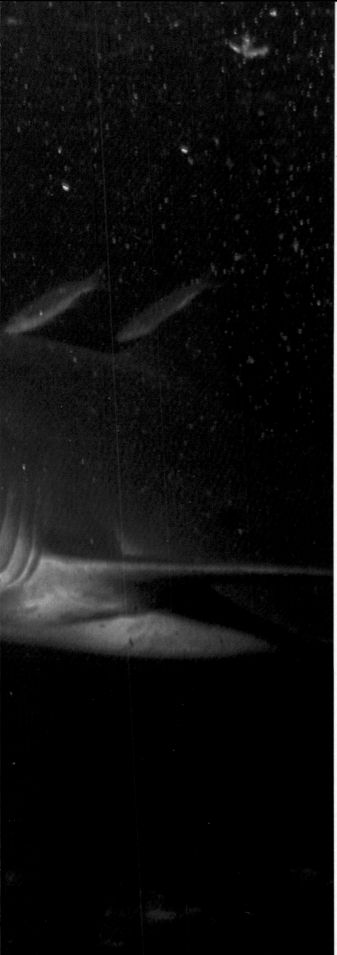

Chapter One
ATTACK

In reality, of the 350 or so recognized species of sharks, only 30 have been known to attack man. Of those, the great white, the tiger, the hammerhead, the bull, the grey nurse, the oceanic white-tip, the mako and the blacktip figure strongly in the records, but fortunately most of them find human flesh so unpalatable that they readily spit us out!

Danger — myth or reality?

The newspaper headlines underline our morbid fascination: *Jaws! Swimmers Dash from Sea in Shark Panic, Beach Fear as Shark Eats Man* and *Jaws Hunt for Suspect Killer Shark*. However statistics reveal that more people die in road accidents during a holiday weekend than have been killed by sharks worldwide in the last 10 years. But the fact remains that sharks *do* attack people and these attacks are quick and terrible. Sharks, though, are generally not man-*eaters*, but man-*attackers* — a subtlety, perhaps, lost on their victims.

Preparing for attack

When sharks attack they use all their senses, making them formidable hunters and killers. At about ⅓ mile (½ km) a shark can smell blood or body fluids in water, and follow an olfactory corridor to head upcurrent towards a victim. At 500ft (150 m) a shark can hear and accurately locate the low frequency sounds of commotion in the water. At 65ft (20 m), and almost in the dark, it can see the movement of the prey. And, when it closes in for the final attack, sensory organs guide it to the victim.

When sharks close in for a final attack a membrane covers and protects the eye from struggling prey, so the shark is essentially swimming blind.It is guided in over the last few yards through a remarkable sensory system, located in the snout, which picks up minute electrical currents, given off by its victim's (often frenetic) muscular activity.

Although the shark's bite is powerful, the main damage is caused by the shearing action of the teeth. A shark has an endless conveyor belt of teeth, and they are probably replaced about five times a year. Its efficiency is increased through miniature teeth all over the body which trap mucous and reduce resistance in the water, so making the fish hydrodynamically silent. Swimming speed in mackerel sharks, like the great white and mako, is increased by keeping the immensely powerful swimming muscles a few degrees warmer than the surrounding seawater.

Plan of attack

According to one shark expert: "There are two recognizable patterns of shark attack. The first is a quiet approach, where the shark will almost casually grab the victim and produce a severe wound, shake the person around a little bit and then leave. The other is more violent, when the shark will strike repeatedly in a frenzied fashion, producing severe wounds. Death of the victim is the likely outcome of the struggle."

Left: *A fierce-looking sand tiger, or ragged-tooth shark.*

When sharks do decide to attack humans it is clear that nowhere on the beach is safe, even when paddling at the water's edge. An attack can occur in any depth of water, but the real risk of shark attack increases as you move further from the shore. The deeper the water the more you are in the shark's domain and consequently the further you are from help.

Case histories

• On Rivera Beach, Florida, in August 1966, an eight-year-old boy and his mother were paddling in about 1 foot (30 centimetres) of water when a shark charged at the boy. His mother whisked him away in the nick of time and the shark, carried on by its own momentum, ended up on the sand. There it thrashed about until a wave washed it back out. Curiously, as the mother and boy walked along the shoreline, well clear of the water, several sharks followed them.

• A group of sharks were gathered around a fisherman who was gutting and washing his morning's catch at the water's edge. A macho tourist skin diver, out to prove his courage, harpooned one of them. Immediately the shark went berserk. It swam rapidly away breaking the line, shook the harpoon out and returned. To the astonishment of the diver the shark leapt out of the water right up onto the beach, tried to grab him in its jaws, and returned to the sea on the next wave.

• On Monday, 21st November 1983 the Philippines ferry Dona Casandra sank and sharks, guided by their acute sensory systems, arrived swiftly and attacked passengers. One survivor later described how a 2ft (½m) long "baby" suddenly went for his leg. (Surprisingly, the majority of attacks on humans are by sharks less than 6½ft(2m) long.)

Above: *Survivors of Australian great white shark attacks examine the huge bites taken out of a shark by other great whites. Henri Bource (above and top right) lost his leg twice in attacks – first his real leg and then his artificial one! The savagery and unpredictability of great white attacks was epitomized in the horror film* Jaws *(inset bottom).*

Far left: *To prevent damage from struggling prey a nictitating membrane covers and protects the eyes of some sharks.*

Above: *A confused great white attempts to take a chunk from a shark cage.*

Left: *Blood from a potential victim in the water can be detected by a shark from a quarter of a mile away. The ensuing encounter may result in the shark going berserk in a "feeding frenzy".*

Below: *The distinctive shape of the hammerhead shark which has its mouth on the underside of its broad head.*

Sensory cells in minute jelly-filled pits (known as the ampullae of Lorenzini) all around the snout of the shark can detect very weak electric currents produced by the prey. In this way bottom-dwelling sharks can accurately locate and catch flat fishes hidden below sand or gravel on the seabed. Other sharks use the sense to home-in on their targets during the last few "blind" inches, when protective membrane covers their eyes.

Great white sharks are thought to be confused by the small galvanic currents produced in seawater by the metal bars and floats of shark cages (left) and outboard motors (above). Much to the consternation of skin-divers and crew members, the sharks often ignore the bait hanging over the side of the boat and repeatedly attack and attempt to bite, in a frenzied fashion, these metal structures. In the same way attacking sharks may find the metal fittings on scuba diving equipment particularly attractive.

Great white sharks, found near Dangerous Reef off the coast of South Australia, are "teased" with baits of horse-flesh (below and right). The fish (right) is severing in two the leg of a horse with one enormous bite.

Great whites are fast and agile swimmers (far right). Their torpedo shape and huge flattened tails are hydrodynamically near-perfect. The blood vessels supplying the powerful swimming muscles are arranged in a "heat-exchanger" configuration to conserve heat. This enables the shark to maintain its muscles at a temperature a few degrees above that of the surrounding seawater, thereby making it more efficient and all the more powerful.

When a great white shark attacks a large victim, the jaws are pushed forward, level with the upturned snout (far left), so it does not have to turn on its side to grasp its prey. Both the top and bottom teeth of the great white (bottom left) are characteristically triangular and serrated.

The shark tears away a portion of its prey, usually chunks from a large dead whale or living seal, sea lion or elephant seal, with violent sideways movements of the head. A great white can cram 100lbs (45kg) of food into its stomach in one meal, which will last it three months. The teeth of the mako shark (top left) are more pointed for impaling fish. In most sharks the teeth are on a "conveyor belt", with new ones forming continually behind those currently in use. Some sharks have just one row, others several rows, but all lose their teeth constantly. The replacement rate for lemon sharks is one tooth every eight days. A single shark may produce thousands of teeth during its lifetime.

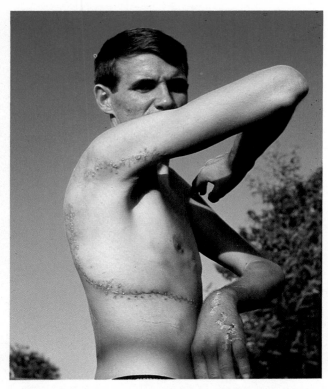

The monstrous gape of a great white shark can inflict
enormous wounds and leave giant bite-size scars on shark
attack survivors. Often the species of shark is identified by
the teeth it leaves behind, or by the size and shape of the
wounds. Curiously, the majority of shark attacks involve
only one bite or slash, which has led some shark researchers
to conclude that most attacks are not motivated by hunger.
Some survivors have been picked up by large sharks, shaken
like toys and then spat out. Even a shark brushing past a
swimmer can result in serious abrasions, since the shark's
skin is covered with dermal denticles or little teeth.
Consequently some societies use shark skin for smoothing
down wood, much as we would use sandpaper.

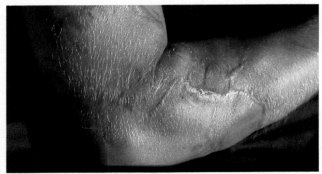

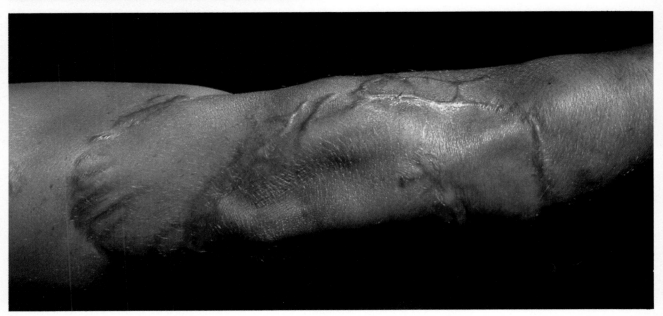

Chapter Two
THE GREAT WHITE

The great white shark, otherwise known as the "man-eater", is a celebrity, thanks to Peter Benchley's *Jaws*, and the only predictable thing about a great white is its unpredictability. Great whites attack anything, at any time and without warning, but they do not usually eat their victims. After the initial bite, the person is often released, although survival depends on whether the shark has severed any major arteries. One sinister interpretation put on this kind of behavior is that the shark is maiming its victim then letting it bleed to death before eating it.

American great whites
Attacks by great whites have been most prevalent along a 124 mile (200 kilometres) stretch of California's coast from San Francisco in the north to Monterey in the south. The most northerly attack along the north American Atlantic coast was at Buzzard's Bay, Massachusetts in July 1936. A swimmer in water only 10ft (3 m) deep was attacked by a great white. Though rescued, the swimmer later died in hospital.

Formidable killer
In July 1916, at the time when many thousands of soldiers were being slaughtered in Europe, a series of 5 attacks in 10 days along the New Jersey coast became front page news. Perhaps the most horrific was described in David Baldridge's fascinating book, *Shark Attack:*

One of the boys dived from a piling into the murky water and, after having felt something rough grate across his midsection, clambered from the water to find his stomach streaked with blood. He cautioned his friends, 'Don't dive in any more — there's a shark or something in there!' But soon he too ignored even his own warning by again diving into the creek. Sometime later, 12-year-old Lester Sitwell called to a friend who was about to climb out of the water, 'Watch me float, fellas!'

As the other boy turned to watch Lester, he felt something slam against his leg and looked down to see what appeared to be the tail of a huge fish. It was heading straight for his friend. Young Sitwell screamed and in an instant was pulled down into the dark depths of Matawan Creek ... the creek became crowded with would-be rescuers, some in boats and others diving into the murky water not yet fully realizing what had happened and the fate that possibly awaited them just below the surface of the creek.

One brave would-be rescuer, Stanley Fisher, dived several times into a deeper section of the creek. A stain

A great white uses its shearing teeth to rip away chunks of horse flesh, being used as bait. The jaws can close with a pressure of 20 tons per square inch. The teeth have the same hardness as steel.

of blood appeared around him and, according to one report, he emerged from the water holding his severed right leg above his head. He died later in hospital.

Several sharks were caught near the creek but attention focussed on an 8½ft (2.6 m) long great white which was found to have about 15½ pounds (seven kilograms) of human flesh together with a boy's shin bone and a rib bone in its stomach.

The great white shark is the largest known predatory fish in the sea, but several million years ago an even larger predatory shark swam and terrorised the oceans of the world. Its scientific name is Carcharodon megalodon, *and we know of its existence from 5 inch (127mm) long fossil teeth* (right). *Shark experts, comparing these teeth with the teeth and jaws of the living relative, estimate megalodon's jaws to have been 9ft (2¾m) across, with a body length of about 50ft (15¼m) or more.*

"Living fossils", like ceolocanths, that were thought to have become extinct millions of years ago, have been turning up with unfailing regularity. So it's quite possible that the megalodon is still living and breeding in the sea's depths.

Sharks can turn cannibalistic. The great white (above), when hooked, is often savaged by others of its own species. And in sand tiger sharks, which give birth to live young, the embryonic sharks inside the mother attack and kill each other until the fiercest and fittest is left. Having eaten its womb mates it then spends the rest of its confinement gobbling down eggs produced by the mother.

Such aggressiveness became painfully clear to one marine biologist who thrust his hand inside a freshly disected 8ft (2.5m) long female sand tiger shark and was promptly attacked on the thumb by a 3ft (1m) long youngster which was lurking inside.

Sharks that have been hooked or speared and then landed are often used by scientists for tests. The eye, for example, clearly visible on this great white (left), has been found to be many times more sensitive to low levels of light, such as those found below the sea (above), than is the eye of a man.

Sharks are nocturnal hunters, so in areas where sharks occur it is best to keep out of the water at night. Some sharks appear to see well in color, although being restricted to blues, greens and yellows. Tests with lemon sharks have shown that they can distinguish red from white colored discs, but cannot tell a square target from a round one.

Sound is important to underwater creatures. Sharks, although silent themselves, use it to locate their prey. The low frequency sounds associated with a struggling fish or a sick seal may attract a blue shark (left) or a great white (above) from a considerable distance. Playback experiments with underwater loudspeakers have shown that many species of sharks can be attracted within minutes to sounds between 25 to 50 Hz, which are at the lower end of human hearing.

One researcher noticed that the sounds given off by the rotor-blades of helicopters attract sharks, thereby endangering the lives of those requiring an air-sea rescue in shark-infested waters. Irregular sounds, like those given off by a swimmer thrashing about in the water, are particularly interesting to hungry sharks.

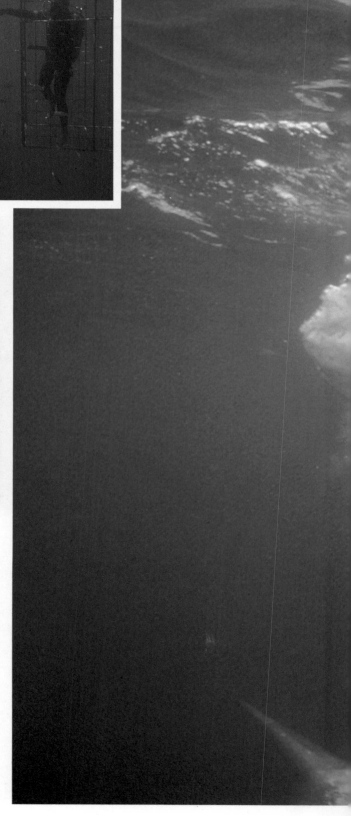

Great white sharks at Dangerous Reef, South Australia, being attracted to mashed-up blood and guts in "rubby-dubby" slicks that drift away from the diving boat. Having homed-in on the source of the smell the sharks are induced to "perform" in front of the movie camera (right) with the aid of chunks of horse meat.

Feeding an enormous great white by hand (above and top) might seem exciting, but the shark could just as easily turn on the flimsy cage and rip it apart, winkling out a tastier morsel from inside.

Spear fishermen use harpoons with an explosive head in order to ensure their own survival in an encounter with a large great white shark (right). The ultimate trophy is brought ashore (left). Another great white (below) takes a bait and swallows it whole.

"Beauty and the beast" — *Australian skin diver Valerie Taylor* (left) *who, together with her husband Ron, has taken some of the most exciting footage of great white sharks and a multitude of other creatures from the sea, and brought the underwater world to countless homes around the globe via films and television. Perhaps their most successful venture was making the movie* Blue Water, White Death *(1971), with Stan Waterman and Peter Gimbel, that included scenes of three huge great white sharks at Dangerous Reef.*

A great white (right) *approaches the stern of the diving boat but ignores the bait and instead attacks the metal diving platform. It could well be confused by the electric currents given off in the water by the metal, unless it is more interested in Valerie Taylor's feet!*

Some marine biologists consider the great white shark an endangered species. The jaws (below) *when removed from the head, cleaned and mounted, will fetch upwards of a thousand dollars on the open market. There is a considerable demand from tourists to own a set of great white jaws.*

Chapter Three
MEDITERRANEAN & BRITISH SHARKS

It may come as a surprise to British swimmers but they need not look very far for potentially dangerous sharks! In British waters the mako and the porbeagle belong to the notorious group of mackerel sharks, first cousins to the great white.

Dangerous waters

Great whites are found in the Mediterranean and they frequent the eastern Atlantic. In December 1979, off the north coast of Madeira, south-east of the Azores, a swimmer was killed by a great white shark, the first attack in the island's history.

Porbeagles have attacked and killed in the Mediterranean and makos have often savaged small boats. In August 1983 Greek harbor police warned holidaymakers on the Aegean Islands that large sharks were about. Two 13ft (4 m) long specimens had been killed in the area that month.

A British species of shark, the thresher, has an enormous sickle-shaped tail, and has been known to approach small craft along the south coast of England. In June 1981 a thresher almost 13ft (4 m) long leapt into a 23ft (7 m) long boat filled with anglers fishing off the Isle of Wight.

"It turned towards the boat and dived", remembered one of the fishermen. "Everything was quiet ... then there was a great rushing noise and suddenly the shark came out of the water, about 15 ft (4½ m) away. It landed across the boat and the impact nearly sank us, but it killed the shark outright!"

Around British shores there have been only a few recorded shark attacks. One occurred off Scotland, near Wick, when a fisherman was mauled. Another scare took place at Folkestone where two children were swept off their feet by the long tail of a thresher. At Swanage in Dorset two anglers were trapped against rocks by three angry threshers, and throughout July 1983 large numbers of threshers, chasing a superabundance of mackerel, scared bathers from beaches around Bournemouth and Christchurch in southern England. At Beesands, in south Devon, a mako shark went for a lone skindiver, not far from the beach.

Shark versus diver

In 1972 some groups of scuba divers were on the Manacles Reef, south of Cornwall. As they reached the surface their leader spotted trouble.

"I noticed that two divers had already surfaced and were giving what seemed to be a distress signal. I noticed that a shark's fin was circling the two divers, so I said to the skipper of the support boat: 'We'd better pick those two up'. He said: 'No boy, don't

The jaws of a captured mako shark showing the many rows of fang-like, "fish-trapping" teeth.

worry about it, it's only a basking shark'. But I could see that the two were definitely agitated and were giving very firm distress signals.

"When we reached them they were back to back with knives out, and the shark was circling them intently. We got the boat between the shark and the divers, lifted the diving set off one of the divers and helped him aboard. Suddenly the shark stopped circling, faced the diver and came forward rapidly. I shouted to the others to get the chap on board and we lifted him bodily, equipment and all, clear of the water. At the same time the shark swam under the boat at the point where the diver had only a couple of seconds before been floating in the water. That was the last we saw of the shark."

In British waters, the mako (above) *and the porbeagle* (right) *are first cousins to the great white. They are commonly caught during the summer months around the south-west of England and all along the south coast. The mako is one of the fastest and most aggressive of sharks. Often it leaps 20ft (6m) high into the air when hooked, and has been known to come in over the back of the shark fishing boat injuring the occupants. The largest porbeagle caught was 8ft 4in (2½m) long. Porbeagle steaks, marinated in white wine, are considered a delicacy in France.*

Another lively British species is the thresher shark (inset) *with its very long sickle-shaped tail that it uses to round up small fish. It often comes close inshore during the summer, chasing large shoals of mackerel.*

The whale shark (left) is the largest known fish in the sea.
It is harmless, feeding on the vast quantities of zooplankton
floating in the upper layers of the ocean. It can grow from
40–50ft (12–15¼m) long, and is characterized by the rows
of white dots all over the body. The whale shark is an egg
layer. An egg case that looked very much like a dogfish
"mermaid's purse", an extraordinary 27 by 16 inches (68 by
40cm), was once dredged up from the bottom of the sea near
Port Isabel, Texas.

The blue shark (above) is one of the smaller predatory
sharks, although large males have been known to grow to
12ft (3½m) long. Note the nictitating membrane covering
the eye as the shark bites into the bait-fish.

45

A blue shark (left) cruises just below the sea's surface in the English Channel. The blue is the most commonly caught shark in British waters.

A basking shark (below) is brought alongside. It is the largest shark to be found in British waters, growing up to 30ft (9m) or more, and is the second largest known fish in the sea. Like the whale shark, it is a plankton feeder and is relatively harmless, although the powerful tail can easily upset a small boat.

A basking shark, towing a transmitter, was recently tracked from a space satellite in an attempt to find out where the fish go in winter. It is thought that they rest on the bottom of the sea where they molt their gill strakers.

One unusual aspect of the basking shark's behavior is that occasionally it leaps clear of the water. It is thought that this activity dislodges parasites.

Hammerhead sharks (right) often congregate in large numbers, particularly around coral heads in the Gulf of California, in the Gulf of Mexico and along the Florida coast in the western Atlantic, presumably for mating purposes. Anatomists have found that hammerheads have a special muscle that enables the shark to move its broad head up and down, much like the elevator in an aircraft's tail.

Sports fishermen (below) and scientists have undertaken a cooperative program in the tagging of sharks in an attempt to ascertain numbers, movements and the general biology of sharks.

Blue sharks (left) have been found to undergo tremendous migrations around the North Atlantic Ocean following the gyre in a clockwise fashion. Curiously, though, only the females make the journey, the larger males remaining off the coast of North America. Sharks tagged off Long Island have been recaught in the English Channel, in the Mediterranean and off the Azores (right).

The blue shark is the most streamlined of sharks and is characterized by its long pectoral fins and pointed snout. It is colored dark blue above and white below.

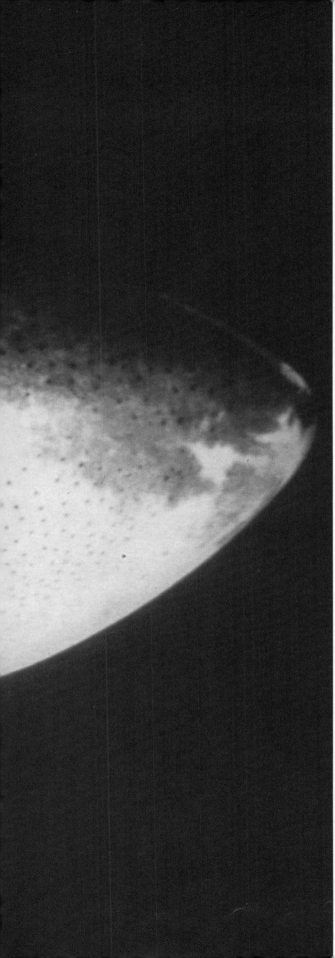

Chapter Four
AMERICAN SHARKS

It has often been suggested that the water must be over 21°C (70°F) before a shark will strike a human. At Siesta Keys, Florida, only 14 per cent of bathers would swim when the water was below 21° C, so most swimming occurs in temperatures conducive to shark attack. It looks as though man's behavior has governed the pattern of shark attack rather than the other way round.

Surf board or supper?
The shark, it seems, has difficulty in recognizing its natural prey. From a shark's point of view surfers on their surf boards might well resemble seals. In the past couple of years, surfboards have become shorter and have curved fins and split tails. This, with the dangling and splashing arms and legs of the surfer, looks very much like a seal behaving in a peculiar way, suggesting a wounded or sick seal and a perfect target to a hungry great white shark!

Shark attacks were infrequent along the coasts of northern California and Oregon. For 20 years from 1952 there were 12 attributed to great whites. From 1972 the frequency of great white attacks doubled and surfers became a prime target. This was about the time that the shorter surfboards began to appear. Since then there have also been 12 attacks. Naturalists at the Point Reyes Bird Observatory have noted that in the early 1970s there had been no more than one or two shark sightings a year round the Farallon Islands, 20 miles (32 kilometres) out to sea from San Francisco, but in 1982 there had been 17. Few attacks had taken place along the southern California coast, only in the north where the seal colonies are found.

Migrations
One of the most important factors affecting the distribution of sharks, both dangerous and harmless, is water temperature. Along the coast of north-east USA, to the north of Cape Hatteras in North Carolina, a recognizable pattern of shark movements and distribution occurs during spring and early summer. An 'Apex Predator' tagging program, where scientists and sports fishermen have cooperated to catch, label and release sharks, has revealed the 20°C (68.5°F) isotherm to be an important feature to follow as it passes northwards up the Atlantic coast.

In May and early June, blue sharks move inshore, over the continental shelf from their deep-water wintering areas in the Sargasso Sea and along the north wall of the Gulf Stream off Bermuda, ahead of the 20°C isotherm. They prefer cool water. Just behind the submarine temperature boundary follow the mako sharks and swordfish that reach the northeast in late June and early July. The hammerhead and tiger sharks prefer the warmer waters in mid and late July. In the fall, the reverse happens and they all return south or into deeper waters. The blue sharks, for instance, have

A close look at the shark's snout reveals the pits for its electric senses.

been found to split into two groups: the large males stay in the western Atlantic, while the females move across to the coasts of Europe, the Azores and Africa, following the clockwise movement of the North Atlantic Gyre.

Cape Hatteras forms an ecological break, as it juts out from the American mainland into the Gulf Stream. To the south, the water temperatures remain relatively constant and the seasonal variations are less marked than in the north. The distribution of apex predators is quite different. Along the Florida coast hammerheads and tiger sharks are to be found all year round.

Protect and survive!

Research into shark defense is being carried out, mainly in the United States, South Africa and Australia.

One of the most effective ways of protecting a beach area from sharks is to fish the local population of sharks out of the water, and so reduce the numbers in order that the mathematical probability of an attack on a bather is minimal. The best way to do this is by meshing — a method used in South Africa and Australia to protect popular bathing beaches.

Meshing consists of a parallel row of nets, with floats

The dorsal fin of a bull shark (above) cutting through the sea surface. The creature is one of the most notorious of sharks, being responsible for many attacks.

An experimental photograph (right), shows that, from a shark's-eye-view, a surfer with arms and legs dangling over the side of a surf board resembles prey in the shape of a floundering seal.

Ignoring danger signs (inset) at shark risk beaches, particularly at night, could make it your last swim!

at the top and weights at the bottom, which are placed across the front of the beach, beyond the line of surf. They are not continuous, like a cage, for outer nets alternate with inner nets. Curiously the system allows the sharks to pass through as they head for shallower water, but catches them on the way out. Their heads get caught in the net, and without any forward motion they cannot breathe and drown.

On one occasion a foolish swimmer entered the meshed area for a night swim, the time when the local shark population is on its way *in*. At dawn they move out and are caught. In Australia, no attacks have occurred at meshed beaches.

The Johnson Shark Screen

The Johnson Shark Screen, developed in the USA, consists of a plastic bag folded up to about the size of a pack of cigarettes.

When in the water, the top is supported by inflatable rings or collars that keep the device afloat. The survivor climbs into the bag, which is filled with water and is submerged. An added advantage is that any blood or other fluids seeping from the survivor is contained inside the bag and therefore does not excite the sharks.

Electrical deterrents

The "Shark Shield" delivers a fairly weak DC current that can be barely felt with the hand, and yet will ward off a shark. It's in the early stages of research and development, but clearly the shark's electric sense is a weak point worth exploiting.

Diver Valerie Taylor entices a shark to bite her while wearing a protective "chain-mail" suit (right). It has proved to be effective against small sharks but is unlikely to provide any real protection against the jaws of a great white (above).

Moses Sole — an unforgettable meal

A chemical which has proved most effective comes from another fish. It's a flatfish, discovered in the Red Sea, and it's particularly repugnant to sharks. The moses sole exudes a milky fluid from the base of its fins which is a toxin. It was tested in the USA on two captive sharks and the moses sole proved to be an unforgettable meal. They took the fish into their mouth but were unable to complete the bite. The sharks jaws were paralysed — with "instant lockjaw" and they went berserk. It has been suggested that a slow release version of the toxin, incorporated in neoprene suits, or a fast acting "shaving stick" device on the end of a shark "billy" might be developed to protect commercial divers.

But tests continue and, until an effective deterrent is found, caution is advised by the world's shark experts. Follow the rules when swimming or diving in waters known to be home to dangerous sharks; otherwise that swim might be the last one you take.

Right: *A dummy is prepared for the initial tests on the "chain-mail" suit.*

Top: *Valerie Taylor attempts to get a large grey nurse shark to bite into the suit to test its effectiveness.*

Left: *A diver fends off an aggressive shark with a "shark billy." The charge in the end of the weapon explodes when it comes in contact with the shark, so killing it.*

Above: *Many beaches in South Africa and Australia are protected by "meshing". Sharks, which can only swim forwards, get their heads caught in the mesh of the net and eventually drown because insufficient oxygen passes across their gills. In its struggle, this hammerhead has firmly trapped itself and will stay there until the meshing boat returns to empty the net.*

During a seven-year period over 7000 sharks were meshed off South African beaches, including about 600 bull sharks (the species responsible for the most attacks in the area), 300 tigers and great whites, and assorted makos, lemon sharks and ragged tooths.

In the Shark Attack file there have been 117 shark attacks recorded around the coast of Africa, including 99 off South Africa. However, the most dangerous waters are off Australia, where there have been 319 recorded attacks. During this same seven-year period the figure for the USA stands at 225. Around the British Isles there have been only three known deliberate attacks.

1

2

3

5

4

TOP TEN KILLERS

1. Great White Shark

Grouped with the porbeagle and the mako as one of the mackerel sharks, this species represents the largest and most powerful predatory fish in the sea.

It is found in all oceans, at all latitudes and is considered to be one of the most dangerous creatures on earth. It can grow up to 30 feet (9 m), and regularly specimens are caught that are 15-16 feet (4.5 − 4.9m) long and weigh in at 3000 pounds (1360kg).

Most are found close to sea mammal colonies along the California coast, off South Africa, and along the South Australia Coast. The north-east coast of the USA, robbed of its seal populations, attracts great whites with the carcasses of large whales.

Note: Most attacks on humans have been cases of mistaken identity − great whites prefer seals.

2. Tiger Shark

A large and aggressive shark, known to exceed 20 feet (7 m) in length, and responsible for attacks in tropical and subtropical seas worldwide. Easily recognized by its broad head with prominent flaps on the nostrils, long-lobed upper tail fin, and a striped pattern on the sides of younger individuals, it is the most feared shark in the Caribbean and the South Pacific Islands.

3. Bull Sharks

A group of sharks that are found inshore, in tropical and subtropical regions, particularly in fresh and brackish waters such as Lake Nicaragua, the Amazon, the Zambezi and the Ganges rivers, and other rivers throughout Africa, Asia and Australasia. They are thought to be responsible for the majority of attacks on swimmers along South Africa's beaches, and have even been known to attack young hippos.

4. Oceanic Whitetip Shark

A very common and very powerful oceanic species that is in attendance in large numbers at air or sea disasters. Easily recognized by the white tips to its fins, the length of its pectoral fins, and the group of pilot fish that often

6

7

8

10

9

swim in front of its snout, this shark has sometimes reached 12 feet (3.65 m) in length and has a global distribution.

5. Whaler Sharks

A group of recognized "mankillers" that include the blue, black and bronze whalers. They grow up to 12 feet (3.65 m) long, and are responsible for many attacks in Australian waters, particularly along the Great Barrier Reef.

6. Hammerhead Sharks

A group of sharks that some people consider dangerous, they are characterized by their curious-shaped head and reduced pectoral fins. It is thought that the broad "hammer" allows the shark a better "view" of its submarine world by separating the eyes and having a larger number of "electrical" sensors to detect prey. The largest species can reach 20 feet (6 m) in length, and they are found in most tropical and subtropical seas.

7. Blue Shark

A very common streamlined shark, with long curved pectoral fins, that grows up to 12 feet (3.65 m). It is found in warm and temperate waters all over the world. Fast and maneuverable, it is often found near rotting

whale carcasses and is likely to turn up after shipwrecks, hunting for scraps of food.

8. Blacktip Reef Shark

A smallish, 2 − 5 feet (0.6 − 1.5 m) long shark found in shallow waters in the Indian and Pacific Oceans. When wading waist-deep watch out for small individuals. Many attacks have been by sharks no longer than 2 feet (0.6m), which can be very agressive.

9. Grey Reef Shark

An inshore shark of tropical waters that shows "aggressive" behavior reminiscent of a fish defending a territory. When it arches its back, drops its pectoral fins and swims with a pronounced weaving pattern, back-off as quickly as possible! Its next action will be to attack with mouth wide open.

10. Sand Tiger Sharks

A group of sharks, sometimes known as the raggedtooths on account of their mouthful of fang-like teeth, that are found in the coastal waters of Australia, South Africa, North and South America, Japan, China and India, and are also known in the Mediterranean. In American waters they are considered harmless, whereas elsewhere they are given a wide berth.

ADVICE FOR SWIMMERS

ADVICE TO BATHERS AND SWIMMERS

Always swim with a companion, and do not wander away from other bathers thereby isolating yourself as a prime target for attack.

Do not swim in water known to be frequented by dangerous sharks. Leave the water if sharks have been recently sighted or are thought to be in the area.

Although not conclusively proven, it is thought that human blood attracts and excites sharks. Keep out of the water if you have open wounds or sores. Women should avoid swimming in the sea during menstrual periods.

Murky or turbid water of limited underwater visibility should be avoided. In any event, a particularly watchful eye should be maintained for shadows and movements in the water. If there is any doubt, get out at once.

Refrain from swimming far from shore where encountering a shark becomes more probable.

Avoid swimming alongside channels or dropoffs to deeper water which provide ready access for a shark.

Leave the water if there are unusual numbers of fish and/or if they are behaving in an erratic manner.

Take no comfort in the sighting of porpoises, for this does NOT mean there aren't any sharks in the area.

● It just might be a good idea to select other than extremely bright clothes for swimwear when in waters known to be inhabited by sharks.

● Avoid uneven tanning of the skin prior to bathing in the sea, for sharks apparently respond to such discontinuities of shading.

● Avoid swimming with an animal such as a dog or a horse, etc.

● Take time to look around carefully before jumping or diving into the sea from a boat.

● Particularly at low tide, look at nearby sandbars or reefs that might have trapped a shark.

● Avoid swimming at dusk or at night when many species of sharks are known to be searching for food.

● Never, in any form or fashion, molest a shark no matter how small it is or how harmless it might appear.

ADVICE TO DIVERS

● NEVER DIVE ALONE. Not only might the very presence of your diving partner deter the shark, but together you have a far better chance of becoming aware of a nearby shark to take effective countermeasures. Furthermore, if something did happen to you, at least there would be assistance close at hand.

● Do not keep captured fish, dead or alive, about your person or tethered to you on a stringer or similar device. Remove all speared or wounded fish from the water immediately.

● Use discretion in the choice of wetsuit colors so that there is no chance whatsoever of being mistaken for the shark's natural prey in that area.

● Do not spear fish in the same region for too long or curious sharks may be drawn to the area by either your quick movements or an accumulation of body juices from the wounded fish.

● Leave the water as soon as possible after sighting a shark of reasonable size, even if it appears to be minding its own business. Use smooth swimming strokes, making no undue commotion in reaching safety of a boat or the shore. To the greatest extent possible, remain submerged where chances are greater for watching the shark and countering its charge if attack occurs. Do NOT count on the shark either circling or passing close at hand without contact before it makes a direct run. It may come straight for you .

● Carry a shark billy or plan to use the butt of a speargun if diving in shark-infested waters. Such devices have been shown to be very effective in keeping an aggressive shark at bay.

● Take full advantage of your submerged position and limits of visibility to be aware always of nearby movements and presences. Shark attack case histories indicate that such vigilance has played a major role in minimising injuries and reducing mortality rates among diver-victims.

● Do not maneuver a shark into a trapped position between yourself and any obstacle such as the beach, reef, sandbar, or possibly even a boat.

● Do not in any way provoke even a small shark — not by spearing, riding, hanging onto its tail, or anything else that might seem like a good idea at the time. Even a very small shark can inflict serious, possibly fatal, injuries.

ADVICE TO VICTIMS

● Use any object at hand to fend off the shark while at the same time not intentionally provoking it further.

● Keep fully in mind the limitations of such devices as powerheads, gas-guns, spearguns, etc., and do not expect them to accomplish the impossible. Such weapons, if used improperly, can incite a shark to attack instead of keeping it at bay.

● Use available spears and knives first to fend off the shark, and attempt to wound the fish only as a last resort.

● Be careful when making aggressive movements towards a shark. It may interpret these as a direct threat instead of being startled and swimming off.

● Once contact has been made or is imminent, fight the shark as best you can. Hit it with your bare hands only as a last resort. Probing the shark's eyes and gills might force it away. Startling it by shouting or blowing bubbles can buy you valuable time.

● Most shark attacks produce wounds that are readily survivable. Bleeding should be controlled as quickly as possible — even before the victim has been bought ashore.

Advice such as this will not stop shark attacks from occurring from time to time. It might not even significantly alter the number of shark attacks. But it might just save your life.

(Adapted from David Baldridge's *Shark Attack*.)

PICTURE ACKNOWLEDGEMENTS

Ardea front cover, front endpaper, half title, title page, 10-11, 12 bottom, 12-13, 13 top, 18, 18-19, 22, 24-25, 26, 27 bottom, 28-29, 29, 30-31, 36 bottom, 37, 38, 39, 50-51, 54-55 top, 56, 56-57, 58 top, 59, 60 top left, center, bottom left, 61 top left, bottom right, back cover **Australian Photo Agency** 8, 9 right **Walt Clayton/Ocean Images, Inc.** 16 bottom **Al Giddings/Ocean Images, Inc.** contents, 15 top, bottom, 20, 21, 23 center, bottom, 27 top, 32, 34 top left, top right, 36 top, 52-53, 60 bottom right **Image Bank** Antonio Bignami 47, Paolo Curto 60 top right, Joe DiMaggio/JoAnne Kalish 46 right, Guido A. Rossi 6-7 right **Terry Kerby/Ocean Images, Inc.** 34-35 **Kobal Collection** 13 bottom **Frank W. Lane** 40-41 **Rich Mula/Ocean Images, Inc.** 32-33 **News Limited of Australia** 9 left **Charles Nicklin/Ocean Images, Inc.** 6-7 bottom **Oxford Scientific Films** 43, Survival Anglia 45, 52 top **Dave Phillips** 62-63 **Rex Features** 31 **Seaphot Limited: Planet Earth Pictures** 17, 23 top, 44-45, 52-53 bottom, 58-59 bottom, 61 top right **ZEFA** 48 left, 54-55 bottom, 61 bottom left

Multimedia Publications (UK) Limited have endeavored to observe the legal requirements with regard to the rights of the suppliers of photographic material.